PISS CAMERON

PISS CAMERON

by

ISBN-13: 978-0997689792
ISBN-10: 099768979X

"Historians will long ponder whether David Cameron was correct to turn his back on Europe at last week's summit. But, thanks to one revelation from the weekend, they will also no doubt ask whether he was in his right mind when doing so.

Cameron, it is said, used his tried-and-tested 'full-bladder technique' to achieve maximum focus and clarity of thought throughout the gruelling nine-hour session in Brussels. During the formal dinner and subsequent horse-trading into the early hours, the prime minister remained intentionally 'desperate for a pee'.

Cameron has reportedly used the technique before, notably during his 'no notes' conference speeches during the early years of his party leadership. He heard about it when watching a Michael Cockerell documentary about the late Conservative politician Enoch Powell a decade beforehand. Powell – best known for his infamous 'Rivers of Blood' speech in 1968 – remarked that he always performed an important speech on a full bladder: 'You should do nothing to decrease the tension before making a big speech. If anything, you should seek to increase it.'"

Leo Hickman
The Guardian
December 12, 2011

Contents

PISS

Crab Race

Every year, in the grim & sour cold of early February, David Cameron & his closest friends gather on a lonesome sandy flat off the north coast of Wales. There, they drink & carouse, in the pretentious style of middle-aged men & grill sausages beside a rented cabin.

It was on this sort of late winter night that Cameron & his men went down to the shore line to watch the night chase the sun off & away over Wales' fat mass. "Black night still ministers the moon," said Cameron. "And the sky lays down her laws."

Small crabs began to poke out from the sand. "Boys! Boys!" shouted Cameron. "The pea-crabs have come out!" The men laughed & winked their toes at the crabs. They took off their jackets & threw them over the crabs, they gathered them up & poured them into each other's pockets. Cameron laughed, "Heehaw! They're tickling me! They're so sharp! Hee hee! Who's ready! I'm ready!"

Off came shirts & they put the jackets back on, still swarming with crabs, & they let the crab-claws scratch at the soft fat on their sides through the linen of their fine pockets. "Whee!" they laughed. "Boys, I want you to listen to me. I want you to take off," said Cameron, smothering a laugh, "take off your trousers & pants." With a cheer, the men stripped to their nudity.

They were lined up, Cameron & the men, wearing their jackets, their pockets stuffed with pea-crab, bellies swinging lowly & chafed by sea-air. Huff, huff, they huffed a few times & grabbed at their penises & huffed & on the mark, each began to piss. After a moment, waiting for the slower tips to release, Cameron hen-whistled & they all began to sprint.

Bursting forward, piss flung from their jumbling cocks. They tried to get a hold on them & aim them down, toward the pea-crabs in the sand. The pea-crabs in the pockets were going mad, raging against the savage racers pissing over their kin & kind. Cameron felt for these pinches, focuses on them to feel them more dearly. Crab-cut trills of blood joined in the sodden flats with the piss & sea-spray passing down his legs.

Driven on by the claw pricks, Cameron's eyes sharped & whet on particular crabs, targetting, blasting them off small dunes or blowing them back into holes with a hard ace of piss. The other men kept to spraying their piss, or swinging it into the runners bestride or if they fell behind, pissing on departing ankles. In this way, each man was drained of piss, & by the rules, had to stand where the last drop fell. That is how seven middle-aged men in suit-coats came to be on a dark welsh beach, heaving from exertion, twitching from the snips of pea-crabs in their pockets, & watching as Cameron ran on.

Cameron's back was rail-straight & his arms were square-angles at the elbow, with fingers extended like fish-fins. The wind fluttered the tail of his jacket, baring up over his ass. His prick stood out, pissing a line in the sand to chase.

Quite a heavy stone had been set, where last year Cameron had finally run out of his piss, but he was at that stone & past it now. He ran on, leaping through a small bolt of trees, his legs worn & chappy, but the piss shot like a chain, dragging him onward. "Maybe I'll never run out!" he hollered, to no-one, no-one was near him, his men only heard a victory yelp.

"Another year, another race gone to Piss Cameron!" they cheered.

Tired, & on wet sand, & with no lights to see by, a misstep was heading for Cameron. Rhythms met in the water & a wave began to form. The wavelength burrowed & rolled. Cameron's feet struck the wet sand & piss soured the sea-foam. The crabs frenzied & blood fell. When the wave beached, it swung his legs out from under him, flung him & his piss in the spray.

The wave receded in a rush & Cameron was hard fallen on the sand. Inside his left pocket, were two dozen tiny pea-crabs, crushed. He groaned & creaks came out of his suddenly sea-cold hips as he wrung himself up on his hands & knees. His penis hung, still pissing, pattering a moonscape into the sand. In Cameron's right pocket, the other-side pea-crabs, disturbed by the drop, by the sound of brothers & sisters breaking, started to frenzy. First, they shredded the pocket lining. Then they loosed themselves over Cameron's bruising & sand-swathed body, clipping at his thighs & earlobes, at the spout of his foreskin. They scrabbled over his mouth & eyes & in through his hair, pricked his nipples & opened a thousand scratches with vicious little nippers.

Dazed, the prime minister clenched himself repeatedly, the piss firing in spasmodic trills. He started to bellow for the men. "I think I've hurt myself!" said Cameron, "the crabs have got me, I have fallen down!" His pride rose. "And yet! Still I piss!"

The men came for Cameron across the beach, with a wobbling straight-legged run, their tits & bellies & jowls woofing & tight. They came to Cameron, on his sprawled body, tatted in tiny lines of blood over his length & breadth, halting & jolting pours of piss out onto the sand.

A wave came in, as Cameron shot a last flash. The wave lifted him off the beach & rinsed him clean of blood & sand. His men wrestled him up off the sand & held him up. They walked him back toward the cabin. Only Cameron knew that their crab runs were finished, but he felt nothing about it. He just laughed his rough laugh, gave his penis gave a small twitch & thought of the crabs & the last crab race.

Bar Bet

The bar chanted "Bet, bet, bet," their five-pound notes stacked on the bar.

Over a car? He nodded.

Not a drop spilled? He nodded again.

Vigorous, two-pint Prime Minister Cameron had boasted that he could piss over any car to be found on the immediate block. Now late-stage drunk, mute & watery-eyed Cameron was wobbling. The barflies & soaks pushed him out the door & hooted. "Spill out," said Terry the barman, "Find me the biggest fucking auto around!"

Two women started to hollar from a side-street that they had something & the bar met at a gleaming station wagon, paneled in forest-palette greens & browns & long as a bus. Somehow, Cameron was absent. The jeers started & were followed by demanded bets be paid but Terry ignored them & began to shout, "You thin-prick, you cock-bite, come here, you fat fucking jowl, come on, dregs-and-vomit, get over here or we'll start a riot in your rotten name." Then he hooted & the crowd hooted & they started a chant of his name.

"I'm here," said the Prime Minister, pushing his way through the ring of dozen drunks. "I'm right here."

"Get round, get round & watch me now," called Terry, like a carnival screamer, "Here stands our dear Cameron, who claims he can piss full over an auto, without a splash, without a drop."

"It's no claim, I can!" said Cameron, climbing up on the hood of the station wagon. "I can piss it, long-ways & wide, who doubts me?" Terry started to laugh & he lost his barker cadence. What kind of night was this, it felt mad, but melancholic, like already over. Cameron watched the barman's waver & gave him a curling sneer. "Length or width, what do you people demand?"

Long-ways, long-ways, chanted the crowd, pulling the smiling Cameron down from the hood & setting him in front of the car. A humming off-count chorus starts, piss piss piss piss, Cameron mouthed his own piss mantras, quiet, eyes closed. "Ready?" Terry shouted. "Set? Pow!"

Cameron tore off his belt & pulled out the dick, wrenching at the top like a stuck fast pickle lid— & like a lariat, unfurled piss from his knobby prick. His fingers were dug into the base & he twisted the end of the penis around his finger, keeping the pisshole straight & the urethra pulled to its limit.

"It's gone over," shouted one of the women, "It's all the way over!" Arcing the car, it was a six-meter strand of unbreaking piss. Cameron grimaced, he howled, his mouth spread open, the piss fired out from him. The bar mob let out a cheer & Terry smiled & sank against a graffitied microcar.

Cameron powered some more piss, then grabbed hold of the head of his penis & pinched the tip to cut off the stream. The long tail of the soared off, clearing the station wagon, but piss shuddered from Cameron's prick, he struggled with it, it kept pouring through his frustrated hands. Victorious, but he spent his moment hunched on his own spurting cock, wetting his trousers & shoes, until the piss slowed to a drool. He stood up straight, carnation-cheeked. The car was clean. The car had not a drop of piss on it.

"There it is." he said. No one heard him over the cheering. "There it is!" he tried to shout. His voice was hoarse & quiet. "There it is!" he tried again. "There it is!"

The crowd ignored him & grabbed him up, put him on shoulders (soaking the wool of their coat-backs), shouting piss, piss, piss, piss, all the long way back to the bar.

Only Terry the barman stayed, laughing soft laughs to himself & measuring the length of the car in his boots. "Clear over," he muttered, "Clear over," he repeated, as if someone was still listening, trying, already, to remember it.

Tiny Oak

The piss slipped out of Cameron's dick, playfully, silently. The dandelion heads bowed under the weight of it.

In a mock imperial voice, he began ordering the flowers around. "Bend before me, under my whip!" He flicked his cock & sprayed a patch of clover. He drug the piss back & forth over the bed, the meager dandelions rose & fell like great sunflowers, caught by their own citrine sovereign.

It was Cameron's eye that distracted him, onto a seedling, a tiny oak, rising only a few inches out of the ground, just one step away. "Oh ho ho, little tree, time to bend your bough!" Cameron hollered. He arced his piss & flung thick drops over the patch. "Yield! Yield!" The seedling stayed up, it was as thick as a kite-string, but strong. Piss fell hard, tilling into the dirt around the base.

"Yield & so will I, you tiny tree!" he was still hollaring at it. "Yield, or soak up my piss, & grow up sickly & sour!" But the seedling held.

No matter how Cameron raged, how he pissed & so the petty & playful turned to anger. "Bend you fucking bug, you nothing!" He pounded piss into the weakest, highest stem, & when still unbent, he aimed his piss for the dirt around the shallow roots. Under the pressure, the ground weakened, the piss began to power & furrow, & mud sprayed across the grass. Cameron screamed.

Above sopping earth & below the sound of slapping piss, below the sound of an unending scream, the ground & the seedling began to waver. The hair-thin roots started to tear. It took on a lean. The puddle of piss grew deeper. Cameron saw the weakness in the plant & a grin tore his face. What he did was, he circled the plant in an assaultive moat, & creeping closer, went to his knees before the baby tree. The piss had dug just under the main angle of roots, making a lip. Soaking up through his trouser threads was pissful mud. His jets wiggled at the lip like a loose tooth, working it free of the ground. With a final press, he pissed it loose & the seedling tore.

It skidded across the washed out grass & landed, dying. From his knees, Cameron toyed with the corpse, pissing at it & sending it a few yards further, before he fell dry. He dropped his cock & howled.

The knees burned & the trousers were ruined. Where the seedling had been, was now a torn maw, with a puddle of piss & foam, piss & foam & mud. Cameron stood & quoted the scene to itself. "A puddle of piss & foam. Piss & foam & mud." He stood & walked back to the manor.

Bathroom Call

Cameron opened the door & appraised himself of the bathroom. Tap, one, antique handled, whale bone, with a dorsal crack. Spout, amber plastic. Toilet, one, wooden bowl & seat, iron tank, full of cool streamwater. Inside the toilet bowl, a diorama, carved, small, a field of smiling pigs.

Cameron laughed. "Perhaps piss & shit can stick on the pigs, but it is certainly more entertaining than a smooth bowl!" Beside the toilet was kept a garderobe, for historical artifact purposes. It was open to the courtyard & let in a terrible chill.

"Puff, puff," said Cameron, swilling the air. He looked over the room & pulled his cock out of his pants. He waddled toward the faucet, & just on the knobs, he dripped a few drops of his piss.

He pinched the bottom of his dick & put his thumb over the hole, making a wide spray of piss over the bench of the garderobe. Along the wall, Cameron tapped his prick against the paint, every foot or so, leaving a wet mark the shape of his pisshole. He looked at the ceiling & frowned, & while he frowned, he waggled his penis up & down, scheming.

He only had so much piss & pissing on the ceiling would be useless. He grunted again, & stopped waggling & began to piss slowly over his hands. When he had soaked the skin, Cameron fluttered & pitched his hands, flinging piss across the ceiling. Then he pissed on the floor, letting the natural slant of a settled house carry this piss in the white grout furrows.

As the air came up through the garderobe chimney, every spot & puddle & tap where Cameron had pissed was steaming, softly.

He jumped over toward the sink & pissed a jot up the snout, smeared his remainders on the doorknob & drooled a swath over the line of pricktip dots on the wall. Looking over the steaming run & sprays, there was only the iron-tank toilet left to sprinkle.

"Curious," said Cameron, pulsing his dick & wagging drops of piss back & forth.

The bowl appeared to a cut from a single piece of wood, & all the little pigs & lumps of hay & delicate hills were of it as well. He rapped twice on the hardwood, on the top of the scene. "Yes, curious." The cock responded with the flat hiss of a spent balloon.

He had been stingy. There was still enough. Now he stood before the toilet & started to piss.

Cameron started from the chain, pissing up to the high-hanging tank, then pissed back & forth over the face of the iron tub. Then he pissed down the pipe from the tank, carefully pissing away the small chips of paint. He paused to adjust & started to piss again at the base. Along the wax seal of the toilet, up the edge of the bowl, the piss poured over in sheets. Cameron felt himself emptying.

One careful stream to ring round the seat, incongruously plastic, Cameron noticed only now, with the false grain running horizontal. The bowl was dry. The pigs, the hay, the hills, were dry. The reservoir over the drain looked to Cameron like a pastoral lake. He pointed toward the smallest pig, & let off a stream of piss onto its head. He pissed to the next pig & tried to stop, to cleanly piss over each pig alone, but finally control failed. It was a violent freedom.

Piss shot through the pigs, ran over & between the pigs, from their tiny crafted ears & ears the size of snowflakes & mustard seeds.

Cameron, he sighed & breathed, the stink of his piss rising in vaporous cloud. "Violent freedom," he sighed & breathed. He was emptied. His body was smaller in the suit & his back was hunched. The air was humid.

He coughed, his eyes red & drunk. He slipped his dick back into his trousers & left the bathroom.

Old Enoch

Cameron tried to will up a piss. He was drunk, too drunk to spit straight, in his hand, bottle of the last wine. He stuck his finger in the bottle's neck to steal some droplets & trying not to eye the mini of american whisky. A grunt. The sound of Cameron trying to will up a piss.

It was about control in the beginning. The teenager chewing on short pens for fake cigarettes, scowling over a book, self-consciously furrowing his forehead to better scrutinize a film, about old Enoch Powell.

"Old Enoch wasn't right but worse, he wasn't wrong," Cameron said proudly, as if that was a new maxim. He had been a child who knew, from instinct, the route to power. Neither the preservation of the same, nor the return of past, if it comes time to take power, the past is always too old. The maxim turned, his fat cow's tongue catching loudly on his teeth. Neither the revolutionary, always either the giant-king of the waifs born to lose, or, if he accidentally wins, only one god in the scrubbed spare pantheon, open to infection & coup. Old Enoch wasn't right but the tragedy was, he wasn't wrong either. The true route to power is always the same one; the counter-defense of the old, the surprising, ingenious, creative defense of the old, the challenging defense of the old, the newest tactic & point of view laid over the oldest prejudice. But the postures of a boy are meaningless. It was the image of the man that animated him to it, "the great man in motion," another of Cameron's wrenched phrases.

Cameron laughed at his fat youth's face, sitting on a stubbornly square end table. "Pretense," he mumbled. But the voice on the film, those words, he still knew by memory, at his root & he spoke them back alive.

> "Powell had been waiting in a side corridor, just off the main room where the Conservatives had gathered. A young West Indian man refilled his water & Powell smiled graciously but said nothing. One of the newspapers made something of this later, but it was misinterpretation; this was Powell, his inimitable rituals before a speech. First, he would pace himself to the podium. It was thirteen steps from his waiting in the wings to the podium, so he paced out thirteen steps in the corridor. He nodded to an imaginary figure & bent his head. Instead of a prayer he recited his favorite line in Aeschylus, 'He does not wish to appear the bravest, but to be the bravest.' The classicist always recited in the Greek. Then he would not speak, his mouth skewered shut with no exceptions, until the messenger would call for him to take his position. His most peculiar trick, however, was one he learned lecturing in Australia. For a day prior to a speech, he did not urinate. He would drink normally & he usually found himself in severe pain by the time the speech was to be made. He claimed that it bound his mind to the task & kept him from deviating from

> the text. 'If there is a power to my speeches,' said Enoch, often, 'it comes from there. Urgency should be in the body, not merely the mind. It makes the words right.'"

That is the phrase young Cameron would repeat, "An urgency in the body," when bounding into arguments with his society friends. He began to not piss before writing papers or giving parties, then before oral exams. He began the term at one day & by the end could go six, nine by the start of the next. His young life spent not pissing before papers, not pissing before exams, keeping 'clean' when out with his father, smiling arrogant & smug oedipal as the older man pisses a dozen times before the bottles run out.

Cameron laughed in the dark. That word come back to him, 'clean'. How beautiful he could be when he was young.

When he was young, it was the piss that tore through lectures & deadlines, as a man, it was piss that conquered & roused up to his height. It was a piss, in the darkness of Labour's long triumph, that kept Cameron's soul. A now, ever in agony, the power Cameron held over himself, he held against the world. When the world turned black, it was piss that ran red coal.

And tonight he is alone. The piss is beyond his control. A swallow of wine dregs & a shake of this penis. Cameron grinds his teeth, eyes open. But tonight, the piss will stay silent.

Gallipot

From the depth of the darksome room, David Cameron's thin white penis shone.

The penis was hung, just into the mouth of a little dish for mixing herbs, a gallipot, rim-ringed with images of doves. A towel draped over Cameron's soft shoulders & his heavy lower-half was slung nude off the end of chair. The gallipot gave off the sound of casual, trickled piss. A grimace & a flick of fingers. The men filed out, except for one, this one anonymous, this Attendant, masked & bagged & waiting. "Hello," said Cameron.

At the whisper, softness in the younger man's shoulders, a slumping Cameron saw & shouted at, "Take off that mask, attendant." The thick head lolled blind for a moment at the reverberated yelp, trying to face the command. Pulling at it, Attendant only wound the rubber collar tighter to the neck, tongue stretching from his mouth to grope the air against the shrouding woolen sack. Cameron laughed at the sight of it, he shook his squatty, verruca body. His two fat arms reached out & swung like swatting harmlessly at the mask, in truth & impact, he was beating at the head of the younger man, driven to beat harder at the sound of helpless gagging.

The man had been set a few feet away from Cameron's red-tufted chair. He had leaned far to hang his cock into the pot, leaned very far to keep his ceremonial posture while slapping the face, Cameron sighed about broken protocols and, pulling his cock out from the pot, stood & stepped to just before over the crouching man, pinched & ripped of the sack & tore down the mask covering the face of Attendant.

"Up," Cameron said. "Up," he repeated. Attendant shook on his knees, in swimming cap & plastic gown. "Up," shouted Cameron. Grabbing him by his arms, Cameron stood him up & looked over his rotten red face, then pulled him by his hackles toward the chair. Toward the gallipot.

The gallipot was small & curved, molded from the same clutch of clay. Embedded in it was a wood handle, inside it was polished, like sea-glass. The doves around the rim & deep in, where the piss has gathered, small geometries, hash lines & patterning triangles. Hands around the chin of the attendant, Cameron sat back to his seat. Locked eyes with the attendant & dipped his penis back into the pot, they gazed on it & Cameron began to piss.

Rush around the pot, the slice of the piss through the curve, piss meets the first piss coming in & makes a rush at the back, the attendant, rapt on the blast of the piss in the pot, by instinct, puts his hands out to catch any as the pot nears full, but Cameron slides up & slows his piss, backs up again & lifts his penis as the rising meets the rim. "This," said Cameron, "is a gallipot full of piss. Some men have had their fill of it, you are a little seed compared to them, don't you think?

For the first time, the attendant spoke, "It's an honor. Honor, an honor," in trash vocal tones. Cameron realized he was pleading.

"Ya!" shouted Cameron. "Ya! You don't be servile! Not in front of the pot! This gallipot of piss, of my piss? Or is this your private property, my piss, do you take it?" Hollar & cry from the attendant & he put his face against the rim & sucked deep gulps of Cameron's knurly piss, this poison jug, his tongue swelled & stinging across his lips, he drawn down like drinking down the sea.

Cameron laughed, "Out now boy," tapping the shoulder of the attendant, "That's a good one," Cameron chuckled, "You won't find the bottom, that's fine, that's fine," & still he drank. "Out of there now," through gnashed teeth, pushing on the attendant's shoulders, "Get off of me," Cameron hammered his fist once soft & then with both of them slapped flat on the back of Attendant.

Instead, the attendant drove himself into the pot, into the piss, letting it soak up his head. He breathed it & the piss ran hot up his nose. From the blows on his back, he began to choke, his head, his little fish lips still yearning inside the unbottomed gallipot, the piss flooding his lungs & sinuses. "More," his sputter, "and more." He jerked the pot out from Cameron's hands & swung it around the room. The gallipot's outside, unvarnished & unground & still-gritted, was scraping bloody rashes across his face, as he drank, he swung round the room to show how greedy he was with it, round the room. In his exuberance, the old wooden handle cracked & fell off. Cameron shrieked.

When the men forced open the chamber door, they saw Cameron, he was crying, he had rent his towel in grief, he was rushing around to the corners, trying to spray piss around the room, trying to recover. Behind him, in plastic garments purring with falling drips of piss, the attendant. Dead & drowned. His head wrenched deep in a gallipot of piss.

Mattress Mash

Cameron rolled awake. The voice of a radio technician murmured a greeting & then began broadcasting confidential data on the secure, prime ministerial wavelength. He was already bored by the day.

His waking had interrupted a nightmare. It was severe. A snail struggling to mount a stone. The blankets had been tossed to the floor.

Cameron picked at the deteriorating edge of his sheet, thin Scots wool, pulled the sheet, which was patterned a violent green clash, swept the sheet, it was patterned to match the curtains, swept the sheet off his body but didn't move. His dick stuck out his sleeping trousers. "Peejays," he said aloud. He delighted at the Americanism. Cameron parted his legs & did a slow leg-lift he learned from television, held them until his muscles shook. "Pilates," he said aloud. He set the legs down, very wide. His prick was still half-hard. Cameron tipped the end of it down with his finger & started to slowly piss between his legs. A swelling delta.

The piss soaked beneath Cameron's thighs & in his mind sprung an image of it, of piss, of it curling through the down mattress. At first it would pour out, like across a broad plain, held by a network of goose-pluck pellicle sheen, held flat in a shallow puddle. On this image, Cameron let himself linger, in lingering, he imagined the first vein of piss to break the flat spell, the first tongue of piss to drop beneath the down-mesh surface. It was a second's pause, his image & the truth of the bed, it was a second's pause & then a thousand fingers of piss flung themselves into the depth of the mattress, Cameron shouting them on. "Plunging flit! Battering piss!" he crowed, his hooks clutching to the sides of the mattress. He shook, shaking the stinking piss further deeper.

Shaking & delighted, gagging, his skin stung, he let his speculative eye down to below the mattress on the bottom-board. He wrung his guts to piss harder in anticipation of the first bleed of urine yellow, a spreading star, striking into the firm white-smoke bottom. His eyes shut tight, his dick spluttering piss across his legs, the line of urine running spikes & spears through matted feathers. At the last speck of piss, Cameron's back wrenched up in spasm, arcing, raised his ass & then pounded him back into the piss, pounded his ass against the piss, "Down! Down through & again!" He raised up his hips, the piss dropped off in sheets, downed his hips, before they hit, piss runs like summer sweat, pounded his hips, against the mattress, he pounded, hips spattering the effort, reddening banners of soured skin running crosses over his sides & back.

Cameron pounded without stopping against the sopping mattress until he wore himself fully out & dropped, limp to the piss-fattened bed. "It must be through by now" he said. There was suddenly no enthusiasm, for the piss-wrecked bed, for the piss-lashed legs, for the pounding campaign, piss banged through goose-down. He could no longer conjure images of the piss in his mind.

Dance

Small tones rose, small notes from the small
end of the piano, drums begin to bang &

he, he Cameron, he full of piss, he stands on
stage. One light, on Cameron, on the bare

wood, his bare feet, lights glint off the piss,
dripping anticipatory, from his cock. Music

rumbles higher, Cameron higher too, he raises
slender arms, each graceful curving, he begins

the dance, begins to piss. Cameron in dance-
wear, black shirt & beach flows, loose, white

handwove linen trousers, prick slung out over
the waistband. From raised position, Cameron

strikes his hands, down palms out, piss spilling
in straightforward arcs, jolts to the beating drum,

lowers himself, Cameron, he bends knees,
thighs hold him, strong unbowed under that

scratchy, piss-blistered skin. The music builds
to shudders, it is Cameron's to kick, he flurries

hands & piss belts & violin wails. Cameron holds
his position, rattles piss along the stagefront.

The sound of drums falls, there is the sound of
piss in the stinging air, hail on hard rocks. Still

low, hands out, now holding his knees, to aim
better his piss, Cameron leaps to turn piss

flung across him like a ribbon. The music lets
up its self-suppression, hammers toward the

room, Cameron leaps again, sails piss across
the stage curtain, leaps from a crouch, jam-

ming piss in between the boards & holds. A
stage breeze sets his rough hair, his trousers

in motion, lunges like in wind like a storm, from
crouched on fours to abstract body, slimline

long in pure air, hanging piss streaming behind.
The rigid, linear piss of the early movement is

furious, romantic shattering yellow, ugly un-
planned splay across his belly, his crotch, thick

flopping penis. Like leaping ecstatic between
bodies of his devoured, Cameron moves faster,

spreads arms further, more animal. Faster,
until he was running, bounding on all his fours,

piss battering & shaking off in bursted clouds,
pounding terrible noise! The ring of the stage

is Cameron's, he has marked it with his
hammered feet & hands & his shot piss,

he is the beastly perimeter. So marked & piss-
slick, he skids, stumbles, limbs more will to run

than, on these slick boards, skill after his staged
typhoon, Cameron falls—

tumbling, hands out, falls— toward back of the
stage, the steel rigging bars, hands out, body

thrusting, thrusting then past his hands, collides,
forehead, nose, teeth collide against the girding,

he falls— the musicians stop, crowd stands to
gasp, some screaming, Cameron lies in his heap,

letting off stray, unfocused squirts of piss, blind
to the response, mouth covered by one limp

hand, he hides his glee, his smile in his hand,
watching some helpful woman try to mount the

stage, police stop her, reassured her quietly. An
audience slow to understand, three hundred

people struck by a notion as the notion appears,
Cameron rises, hoist like on a fisherman's line.

The music breaks angelic choral, loud but dread,
and dreading further & louder as he rises, an

aesthetic, pre-emptory resurrection & no-one
betrayed, they understand, he turns with sparkling

face, his penis hosing piss & roaring with the
applause. Once again he leaps, no trace of the

animal that wrecked & wrought the stage site,
his body now dainty in bends, his piss in sacred

curls. Tour en l'air, tour en l'air, piss à cerclette,
the fouled stage is worse for keeping delight earth-

bound, stage as a shadow of an animal bound
& died, the stage a ring of the rising angel in an

animal's midst & piss, that stage there Cameron
dances, rises his arms, piss in fontaine rhythm,

drapes himself in them, mock bashful, piss follows
to dribble, he clowns open, his smile is palpable,

rind smell of piss palpable, eyes to watch him
make & re-take the stage, he nimbly retreats

to back of the stage, slips his shirt & makes
himself nearly smooth, climbs flat-forward,

approaches the front of the stage, he, his body
and face, smeared wet in his piss. Growing pale

and rosy as exhaustion takes & leaves him, peels
himself up off the wood, raises up, neck crowed

back, he raises as a sprout raises, his stomach
off the stage, his cock out from under him,

pissing, he is pissing, he is raising up pissing,
raised up past his knees, up past his ankles, his

back is tall, his cock downward, loose piss
falls. Music falls behind, Cameron's wet hands

beating hands & he screams, now up on his two
highest big toes, he puts his arms up & lets out

the rest of the piss, eyes strong, this is the final
rise, awareness in the crowd of the progression

to risen greatness, they shriek for him, eyes
strong, he holds on toes, pisses, the stage is

unified around one pole, the pole is the piss, eyes
are strong, small light on him reflects off a painted

piss-bare stage, bare feet pissed over, room glows,
eyes are strong, music peaks, piss stops, eyes close,
light, off, gone.

Doctor

"How long."

"Weeks. I don't know. Weeks. Honestly, I don't know. Five. Five weeks probably."

"Why."

David Cameron was breathing very slowly, deliberately, speaking only on the exhale. "I... wanted to... challenge... myself."

"Have you seen any negative effects. Besides the breathing."

Cameron slid wordlessly off the bench. His normally fulsome face was drooped, souring, & his waist had swollen. He undid the needless belt. Where the trousers had rested was a crease of violet, like cold meat. Striking up from his penis were three jagged stains, stretch-marks, splayed with thick peeling ridges. The skin beneath was threadbare. A thin juice seeped between the fibers. These, Cameron's furrows, were the color of lemons & they were speckled in polyps, skintag black whiskers sprouting from the strained flesh.

"You're expanding too fast. Keeping this piss inside of you, it's causing the skin to tear apart. I don't know why the black bits, though. Maybe the skin is under too much strain. It's reacting, trying to keep itself, & you, together. I can show you the measures, but I'm sure you know what they say. Your kidneys are gone, they're like the little black filaments now. Your liver is sodden. The risk of bursting is now not limited to the bladder, but the stomach as well. The piss is scouring your organs & they are developing weak spots. The yellow rings on your gums is urea that has been pressed up your esophagus. The lungs must be severely compromised. Still you won't piss."

"Doctor," said Cameron, "I have taken a vow. An oath. I don't know which. And don't—" Cameron tried to sound angry for a moment, before the pain in his lungs stopped him & bent him over on the physician's slab.

"And don't," whispered Cameron, "tell me that I'm killing myself. I'll send you away like the last one & the last one & the last one, my piss, as it grows in me, I can feel my powers rising," He huffed for a moment. "And my frayed nation begins to twine back together. Who are you treating, that you don't understand, that I would do all of this for my people?"

A jet of liquid squirted off the rightmost stretchmark, leaving a milky line on the curtain. "I understand," said the doctor quietly, "As much as I can, I understand. I can clean you & ease some of the pain."

The doctor swabbed alcohol over the high, curling lips of Cameron's stretch-marks. They began to crust over a chalky black. He tamped down gauze into Cameron's open, blighted skin, roughing the top layers & sluicing off the gray liquid. A smell rose in the room when the streaks were juiced, like grease on fire, like the smell of struck iron, like a dog's nip. The doctor turned Cameron's eyes away, pulled out a razor, & started to shave off the tags.

Cameron screamed. Each fillip of skin was a twisted node of tar being spun out into bristles of skin, each slice shuddered Cameron like the shaving of nerve endings.

"If I stop now, it will be like I have done nothing," said the Doctor. Cameron gnashed his teeth.

"Pain!" shrieked Cameron. "Pain is not worthless! Pain binds me to this body, so Weak!" trilled Cameron. "These cuts, huuh," a small blot of vomit fell out of his mouth, "The pain is running visible over my eyes!" said Cameron letting off a low squeal, & the voice soared "Pains brook our shoulders! Pain! Pain sours the fleeing mind!" Beneath the screaming, the doctor's hand shook & the blade struck into the taut skin. Piss fired from the hole, slapping the doctor back over his chair.

With a howl, Cameron shoved his hands against the small hole & against the piss erupting. Tears blurred his ruddy face. His febrile mashing against the nick caused the fragile skin to tear further, against the pounding of his two soft fists, his stretched slits broke up, & weeks of piss began flooding across the floor. Stained fermented ugly brown, with pebbles of concretion & coral color clumped strings across the floor.

Cameron's face was hung open in martyr's passion, with three wide gashes run across his lower belly, each slowly draining the last piss. A sound from his mouth, a solemn, unlovely lowing, hollow & scattered like run through a stand of young trees.

"I am bereft, I am bereft, I am bereft," screamed Cameron. He stood for a moment & fell.

The Smell of It

David Cameron pushed his hands in his pocket, absently squeezing his prick open & shut. "Do you know what I miss most?" he asked. "The smell of it." Thick tears lay on his cheeks. "The smell of my piss, when it would fill a room." The students quieted down & waited to hear, as Cameron let the memories overwhelm him.

Cameron saw himself as a child, at his father's home. His piss pounded the wall. He let it splash back on his young belly, souring the air.

He thought of the closet where his mother hung her clothes, of dragging his boyish piss across the sharp synthetic dresses. "My mother wore a sweet german perfume," Cameron said, "and my piss was sweet too, but thin smelling, like the first slate of pond ice. The two notes would spiral, first the perfume, then overwhelming piss, until the air would simply— bloom. When a starling finds a smokestack, she soars & festoons down its column. The perfume was the plume, my piss, the songbird."

Cameron then thought of the electric space heater, brought home by his father when he nearly ten. He told the students about the cool gray rods, how he watched them grow red for the first time, how his young eyes looked & how they must have flashed with inspiration. "It wouldn't be until the Denmark holiday, when my parents left to walk on the black strand, that I let the possibilities overtake me. First, I tried to simply piss on it, but it shut off, automatic. There was a safety switch inside. Still, a gray vapor puffed off & spread across the ceiling & I smelled it just there. It was just there, & possible, I was undeterred. I tried to soak a cloth in piss & feed it through the grate, but the heater was too hot & the cloth itself too pungent. I could only smell burnt towel."

"So actually I was quite clever then, & I found a ribbon. I slid the end of the ribbon into the box & so carefully pissed, letting it slide down the length. The piss then pooled on the tin beneath the rods." The students listened closely, following his cues & laughing when he let them. "I turned on the heater, & put my face as close as I could bear, willing that pool of piss to boil. At the edges, where the piss was thin, it burned & gave the pool a crusted coastline of blood red. In the middle, the piss began to bubble, in a line beneath the lowest coil. It spread rapidly as the heat ran across the flat tin plate."

"Oh! But when the hot piss burst! My round cheeks, already raw from the heat, were speckled & scalded!" squealed Cameron. "Steam & smoke started to roll & the piss smelled like a riot, roast walnuts & gasoline & scotch whiskey, all run together!" His jaw took on a trembling. "So exciting was the smell that I gasped, quite by accident, & took in a full huff of the steaming piss. I tried to hold steady, but I began to gag. I was falling apart at the hems!" Cameron stood & gestured wildly with his hands. "My mind was transported, my skin screamed as the bubbling piss flecked small blisters across my face, my lungs were pierced through… Finally, I choked & fell & lay on my back. I watched the steam rise, watched the air grow thick. Grow soggy. With my piss." With that, Cameron wept.

After a few moments, Cameron dried his tears & made his face hard again, with a set jaw. He stared over the collected students, marking each one of them as if they were his kin. "The smell of piss comes to me sometimes." His voice was soft, a soft chirp, sand blown by the wind. "But I have given everything for you." His tone became forced & aggressive. "And it is that sacrifice which gives us our honour. The honour of enduring our losses. Of volunteering to lose & sacrifice for our country & our nation. In some, you can hear the scream of a soldier's pain. In others, you can hear the absent creak of a country home, sold to pay honest debts. To lose, to sacrifice. The honour is in enduring. The honour that is our birthright."

Cameron paused. "I haven't smelled my piss in nearly a year."

The Final Tale

The clamps closed around Cameron's biceps,
in his banal blue suit, around his thighs, his ankles & his neck.

A small, dense man,
with white hair & skin & a custodian's collared overall
looked though Cameron's eyes
like inspecting a pipe-length.

He nodded at the specimen
and made gruff sounds,
while fixing each clamp to a line in a rig of gridded wire.

Satisfied that the binds were strong, strong enough,
the operator left, sounding *tup tup tup*,
the long walk to his booth,
tup tup.

Somewhere in the black dark of the room's distance,
tup tup tup,
clapping his two little boots,
snakeskin cowboys,
tup tup.

From a booth in that far dark,
a clank, & the mechanism squealed,
and Cameron, in his rig & apparatus,
jerked off the ground. High.

Within a minute,
he was hung up & at an angle,
his face bulged with his blood.

A lamp, bolted at his side,
illuminated his immediate below-him
in a hazy round ring.

Tup tup,
into the light walked back the small custodial man,
he had with him a jurry-rigged pole
with a hanger head taped on it,
reached up, hooked on a rope,
tied to the zipper on Cameron's fly,
pulled the hook, pulled the rope,
and the fly.

Cameron's long penis flopped out of his trousers.
It was wrought, & hung
like a knotted stretch of twine.

Cameron,
now up-raised,
now with cock out,
small man nodding, he walked, tup tup,
back into the dark.
Tup tup tup, Cameron heard a door
and a close. He was fully alone.

A grunt from the machine,
it started to bend Cameron's body,
not for comfort,
to optimize his flow.

The arms were pulled out,
straight shoulders across from elbow to elbow,
forearms up at right angles,
hands dangled & hung loose,
his legs were pinched by the machine's orienting clamp
and forced crossed-legged & forced pushed flat.

Cameron looked like a glyph.
Legs in triangle, body in line,
trident made of his head & his hands,
there was a ceremonial twirl of the cock.
Then Cameron began to piss.

Down the piss fell,
onto a steel dome in the center of the floor,
surrounded by texture, textured like a cantaloupe,
so that piss could cling to it.
Piss fell. Piss coated the dome.
The dome shone, piss fell, sopped in the cracks,
ran down along the texture & soaked it.
The dome shone, now the central roughness shone too.

As the piss soaked out past further from the central rough,
the mediating desert,
it approached fifteen rillets on all sides,
small carved grooves,
to direct & flow the piss,
which had now mounted the grip & started
falling in them,

to their straight arrows,
their bursted right angles
and intersectioned dense-flow collisions.

The speed that Cameron dropped his piss was
a careful speed,
well-controlled to keep the rillets from spilling,
it was a stable & measured piss.
He slowed when it seemed the piss
was snaking too fast around turns
or might splash up at a cross.

The piss stretched out to the edge of the lamp light,
into the dark of the room,
where the rillets now shone along with the roughness
and the dome, but barely, a milky pale chlorine color,
like fatty oils, an electricity-shade,
shining to the end of the lip of the rillets,
out in their spreaded patterns.

When the piss fit the last line of the rillet,
it formed the rillet square,
and the light burst to its full illumination.
Cameron stopped the piss for a moment.
He let the stream settle,
to the far corners.
He listened to the sound of his bones stretching
forward.

A dome,
surrounded by a roughness
that led to small rillets

extended into the dark
in a perfect square,
all shone, all shining.

In the rillets, the symmetrical canals,
the piss swelled to the top of the notches,
it was to be just one more than perfectly full,
to maintain surface tensions,
so Cameron jetted a cautious piss,
observed for overflows,
no movement, cautious piss,
jetted another, no break,
one last lash & there,
on the far right of the square,
the terminus of one rillet breached
and piss began to dribble over the side,
down into the dark.

One moment, two moment,
Cameron began again to piss,
but not the tight line to dome & across the rough,
spray, flitted across the rillets as they overflowed,
doily-map intersticied square flushing & washed out over,
the whole square shone in one,
the new piss pushed in waves
to slide off the old piss downward,
downward, piss flung off the square-edge Earth
into the sea-dark nowhere beside.

Down there, a glow strengthened. It was circular.
A moat, shone.

Cameron pushed his piss harder
and absently hummed a high tone.
The spray became a pour,
shattering off the dome,
into the swath color of the square,
& poured into the moat.

The heavy lamp's shine was weak
one artificial dab
against a resonant deep glow.

As Cameron looked down,
he peered upon himself,
he could see that even as it came out of the penis,
his piss had a glow.
Even before it came out of him,
through his penis,
he could see the glow inside.
Beneath his skin,
he could see veins of
piss circulating & secreting
throughout his obscene body.
Beneath him, the dome shone like a star,
beneath the dome, the square shone too,
beneath the square, the pit,
the piss filled up,
and the shine that had started inside him
was now pounding upward the steep walls of the moat.

The piss filled the moat.
The illumination of the room.
Surface tension.

The piss began to make a sound,
A round rumble then a high rising peal.
The sound of the room.
Spirit tension.

The light filled out all the dark,
and in the hum,
Cameron surveyed the room.
It was a half-kilometer square structure.
There was the dome & the rough & the square
and surrounding the square,
the moat, the circle of light.

But beyond, the outward was plain floor & pale walls,
coated in thick skins of chemical paint,
which was beginning, in pockets,
to billow, to sag, to spool off from
its underlying fixture on the walls
because the stink of the collecting piss
was degrading its bonds,
large bubbles appeared, gestated, sagged & then popped,
with a soft fuss.

From the popped spots of these hung sacks,
rough holes,
which wilted quickly & curled back off the peel,
the thinnest pieces of the membranes crisped,
and cracked apart.
Everywhere across the walls,
these piss-reactive droopings.
Through this, the wall behind the paint was becoming
visible.

Cameron stopped, a second time.
He waited for the last spool of piss
to slide off the swath into the moat.
The moat, brimming, shining, squalling high, it
screamed.

Cameron thrust his hips, drooped his cock down,
his face a purple cluster & grimace,
he began to pump huge.
Piss smashed down against the dome,
battered & dented it,
beat it inverse with force of a hammer.
Cameron bellowed,
another pump & his piss hammered it further,
pump & slam, he pumped the piss,
slammed the dome down,
brayed out from between his thick cheeks,
Cameron pumped a last pump of piss
and the dome was pounded,
nail clear through,
it dropped & a hole stood.

A new sound,
of small grinds
of stone against stone.
Cameron resumed,
not spraying or pumping or slamming.
He fed his piss down below,
carefully into the hole in the heart of the square,
until the moat began to rotate.

Cameron pissed further into the hole,
spurring the rotation. Further into the hole,

filling the moat from the center. Further
into the hole, the moat started to lap & seize, & rise,
it began to swirl, nearly full, further into the
hole, the piss began to swirl & overflow
and onto the floor.

Around the edge of moat,
where the piss waters met their shore,
there were notches.
Eight notches, small catches,
slants, lipped up,
piss, under momentum of the moat,
swirl of the rotation, glowing & gleaming,
caught the catches & spit into the air,
shot up, more distance & more glow,
more spit, as the piss fed & geared inside the moat
and it spun faster
each speckle of piss jetted across the floor in lilts & spurts.

The speed of the gyre was high,
at peak, & the spouts of urine are sweating down the walls.
Cameron wept,
gulping in the tart piss air.
The paint on the walls,
sagged, drooped & peeled,
had melted away completely.

Behind the paint, there was no mural.
The piss had washed away the paint
and coated the walls in glow,
coated a bas-relief
of a grand story.

Cameron kept feeding piss into the hole & the spin
of the moat & the spurting continued,
but now his voice fell out from him & he began to recite
the story,
as it was passed down to him.

"It began with a void in the center. Absence at the heart. The Empty spoke kindly to the Null." Cameron's piss punctuated, syncopated his spoken rhythms.

"The Null was the shining, it shone & grew heavy. It became a form. A half-globe. A dome. When the dome swelled in its nullness, under its weight, it nullified again. It fell into itself. From its absence of absence came its roundness, as the circle of domains. From the circle came the voice, the voice marked on the Empty, & cut lines, & lines began their flow. At first, lines stood hesitant & weak, they broke left or right, they became stronger & went against each other, through each other. Empty spoke through Empty & intersection arose. It turned in on itself, at the most pure angles.

"Emptiness was in fifteen lines, each weak & turned, but together their turns & shyness were each bolstered by each line beside, & in their shared sense, they formed a shape. This was the first square. It was composed of fifteen strains of squared angles. As the square reached its limits, the roundness of the Null centric began to spur, spreading around out into the first Empty sea. From above, from some far elsewhere, a stream began to flow. It filled the hole & drained the lines & fell on the sea bed. The first Null Sea. These, the first waters, were piss & they purified the rounded core & the lines & the square & the sea purified itself, & each remained at the Center of All.

"Once purified, then, silence. For an age it was quiet & flat, as the sea filled & the lines drained their piss. When the sea was full, it lazed until it was not content to remain still, & so motion erupted. The sea turned. Became gyre. Spun. The spontaneous movement of the piss in the circle, of the sea, was the first life. As it spun, it spread its light across the silence."

Here, Cameron's gaze rose to the bas-relief. His penis strained. "With light, comes story. This is where the story becomes story. The beginning."

And then, Cameron was silent.

— . II . —

The piss had been pouring out for hours. Cameron was thin. His skin was blotched from the stink & strain. He was no longer feeding the hole, the spin of the moat carried itself along, he squirted piss in long sprays, scattered them across the room. The carvings across the walls flickered in the glow of his piss. It was time to read them.

"As the sea turned, the light rose & held over the Whole. Some piss shone & other piss came to darkness. Some piss rose to become the air, & scorched by the sunlight, gave the sky its careful hues. The piss of the dark grew hard in its density. It fell from primordial to concretion. It did not shout or scream, it recognized the return to stillness as the greater movement.

"Why remain mute vitality, a reduction of spontaneous creation to the repetition of the same eternal act? No. The piss became the land, against the sea, against the sky. Piss differentiated from piss & shook on the surface & the littoral space. Confusion. What is piss-not-piss? Between this diffuse, this dense, & this wet life, in the charge of their clatter, the first being emerged. And all the beings ever after came from this first confusion, & from the confusions after, the splitting & spread of piss in its variety. The pissed being grew fat & slathered the surfaces, blossomed algaes & fishes, & then men & then kings. All of them were piss."

The reedy sounds of Cameron's voice, piss-burnt, his cowtongue dancing to the punctuation of his droplets. Cameron's eyes fell on the unbearable carving of the first king. "Simple hat on tousseled head. Hands made to look shaking. King's mouth open. Discovery. That the piss flowing down along his legs was not waste or water, but a thread. A thread that stretched back to the beginning. It was the king's right hand grabbing under his dress & flinging piss back to the stars. It was the king's left hand, grabbing under his dress & flinging piss forward, over the heads of all the kings next. Reconciling them. The line of history, of recognition & the power of recognition. The piss that threads through our bodies is not temporary. Not incidental. It is the Always."

By curling & tearing against the restraints & pulling up on his own asshole, Cameron had been able to hoist his penis to piss straight, shooting piss across the statue-face of the first king. It splashed the porous stone & soaked it through. "The history is the history of piss coming to know piss & recognize." As the hoisting rig turned & screamed rusty, Cameron pissed on the old face of the second king & barked his secret name. Cameron clenched his opening to spray harder. With each piss & each king, Cameron said the name & turned further, in this way, he coated the history of men & the world & land & sea. Each name fed the moat. The lake of piss bent hot against itself.

As Cameron's penis kecked across the stone-face kings, the heated piss grew thick. Clumps formed & wriggled the surface like eels, like butter's coalesce, like the hesitation of first yellow light before it pricks the atmosphere. The movement rose. David Cameron's piss was coming to life.

Cameron started to sing the song of the kings, sung before him & always sung, Harmonic of Piss-on-Rock. What had been a ring of brittle stone around the moat was now so saturated & superheated by the spin that it wavered, undulating to the speed of the song. Compressing the vortex. With each compression, waves of piss washed up the esoteric rillet square, & splashed onto the center, the void. Each wave left behind a hummock of pisswax around its edges. Layers of gunk sealed the hole. A new shine, the shape of a dome, in the place of the dome. Gush & flux, wax accumulated, amber-silted piss crumble, chittering with crystals from the hibernation in the depths of Cameron's body.

A dense hump had formed. Cameron gave it a gentle douse with a spit of warm pee. It sealed. It moved. Small limbs appeared. They pulled apart the head & split a small mouth for itself. "History is the name we give to the refinement of the world," whispered the clumped pisswax, drizzled over. The wax raised its face toward the long showerhead of Cameron's penis, its tiny voice strained for him. "Now history has made you. And you have made me. It was your jutty belly where I sloshed & sat, the last wait for me & my type. A long wait for me. Long enough to bud." A smile from the creature. "Now I bloom."

Cameron's pisswax homunc took small steps down the dome. It wetted & sogged its feet, & scampered forward, to the lip of the moat. Swift & unsteady, it rose, & stepped on this swirling pool of its own fluidity, holding on the surface. Small steps, a glide, over the waves & valleys, & it began to skate across the surface of the piss, carving shapes into the wet thickness, cooing & laughing. The small voice slipped through the roaring tide, crawled up the portraits of the old kings, scraped on the walls, made for the apex, Cameron in his rig. The voice reached Cameron & blessed in his ear, "Do you see it? Do you see it? You made this. Your miraculous body has made this."

"No-one could cultivate this pure piss back to life. You could. No-one could. There will be more. We have learned from you. And still, it is your miracle. You have made one, that is enough. Is it enough?" breathed the whisper.

"I move across the surface of the piss, your piss, your piss is dancing on your piss, it is alive. Are you in awe of yourself? Do you want to leave? You can leave. You can go home, you can piss where you please & how long you please. Do you want to leave? Or with me, this small one, do you want to make another? Two & then more than two? Will you stay here? Will you stay? Will you become the No-One?" Cameron's eyes flourished. He stayed quiet. He adjusted his body slightly.

Cameron relaxed & muscles he hadn't loosed in decades fell slack & pisses he hadn't taken in decades poured out of him. Cameron's penis grew wide. The pour fell to flood, flood fell to torrent, the torrent roiled the piss into a sea & the waves bolted high. Beneath the roar, he could hear his creatures, so joyful. The sound of the first touch in a new world.

Cameron closed his eyes. Piss fell.

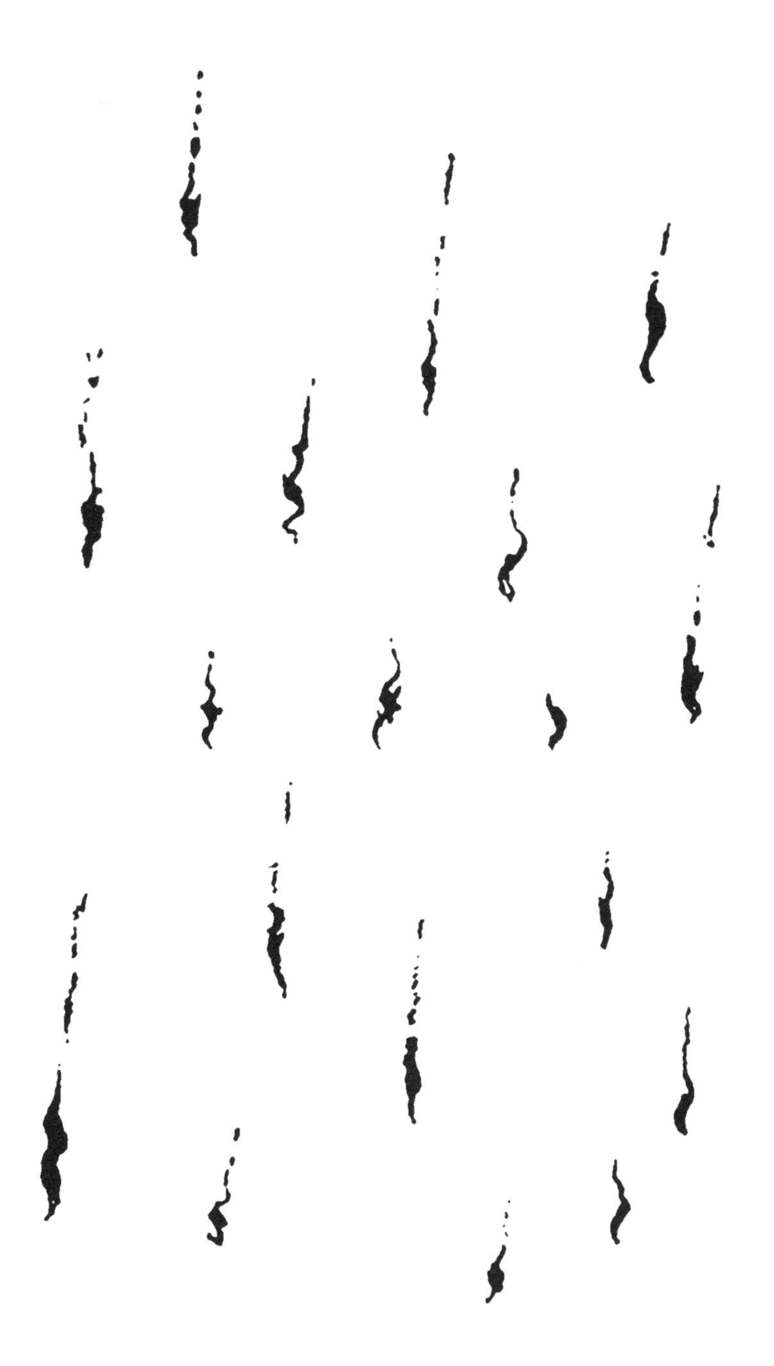

PIGS

When Piss Cameron was re-elected in 2015, I began to despair. This project had exhausted itself, & I had made no headway to informing people that the Prime Minister of the UK derives vigor & insight from the pain of holding his pee. In fact, I seemed to be going backwards, having to re-explain the same story of the EU summit & the smug news leak to the same people. I had become insistent & isolated. Then, in September of that year, it was reported that David Cameron, as a member of a fake secret society, had performed pseudo-occult rituals with his rich dough-faced friends & as part of these rituals, he had fucked a dead pig in that dead pig's face. The disgust I had hoped to empirically associate with Piss Cameron had arrived & I was free of my burdens & of this project. What follows is my farewell.

Pigs Cameron

Love is slow.

While it batters the head & lungs,
two distractions, it is pulling small
rents in the line of successive
events & spreading them out.

As it pulls out its extension,
love turns to terror & delirium,
the splitting of all events into isolated particles.

How to prevent our falling into the undifferentiated,
the anomies of forever-pining,
moments, nights, lovers who continue to rupture?

Sex, a fuck with eyes open,
dramatic bodies & play,
the small terminus of the intellect,
the end of vision, exhausted null.

Sex is the coping with the unstable
temporality of more-than-one together.

And so, perhaps, it overflows its boundary.
Who is always in this falling in love
to have time or desire to combat it?
We are all weary.

No more time for love in its disturbance,
desire's age allows sex to escape into
less dangerous, & less open locations. Play.

Play, sex for play, to explore the twists & textures
inside ones self & some friends,
openings casually wet-fucked on a thursday.

But, then we hesitate, endangered.
We might move away from love but directions
are not arrows, they are paths.
They move in other ways.

So we prepare, to not fall in love this way,
to fuck in this many, rules & boundaries & ethics
for precisely maintaining distant peaks.

Because our practices were meant for another arena.

Creative disturbance is never exactly enough.
Some creeping essent never fully slides off our bodies.
Something dries.

But there is no stopping,
invention returns & through the nest of rules,
we take on new resonance.

There is a resolution,
toward the end,
a point of invention where the problems seem
thoroughly worked out.

What if we don't fuck lovers but things,
fuck in ways removed from responsibility,
from that coping?

What if we fuck out from under exactly that another
who haunted us to fuck in the first place?

There is no rhetoric in a question,
it demands an answer,
what if we did fuck this way?
What have we lost or gained or beyond loss & gain?

Another comes with a softness,
that is, a material texture,
a skin & a flesh underneath, that would be lost.

Another comes with pluralities to explore,
how to be delicate,

Comes with excitations
and troubles of the
meaning of itself.

How to be indelicate, you can fuck in the mouth,
which isn't lonely marked for fucking by
the symbolic order of your time period.

And another comes with this danger
we mean to exclude by our creative act of fucking things,
how to keep from solving our only problem now.

To the pluralities, you put down a body with codes in it.

The danger, you put ritual.
Establish false norms
that prick anyhow at
the catholic level of the lower mind.
Wear a robe & a chain.

To the skin,
the meat,

where is the body without danger,
without taking us back up again?

Is it the place of the dead body,
that gravitation for meaning & desire,
no, because this another is our anonymous future.

Don't want to be skin & meat & fulfill
a program for students to fuck without agon,
don't want to remember we are running such a program.

The human dead body is too close.
It cannot help itself,
it screams about the morality
of its formerly another even louder for not moving.

What has skin & flesh & orifice & codes,
but not so strongly that I get sick or sad or know
myself through the fucking it? A pig.

A pig, a dead pig,
a pig with a mouth & an asshole & hair & eyeballs
& no kick left in it, a pure fucking texture.
We have our plural,
we have our texture,
we have the notion of a ritual but not ritual itself.
Why should we make holy the fucking of pigs?

This would be our dissolution,
the answer to the tearing sound in between us,
and answers are ends & we just wanted simple pleasure.

Simple pleasures lead to experiments,
experiments lead to complex pleasures,
and the memory of the simple always fades in that moment.

Not every day is a day to fuck pigs.

It must be made special, local.
There must be an occasion.
We have to invent the occasion.
And that's how it was, that day,
when we gathered around the pig.

It was in a room,
I checked the lock three times.
There were laughs
but we tried not to.
The pig lay on the table.

The table was dark & the pale animal
had its forelegs hung off the front,
on its side were imprinted
the name of its industrial mother.

There were some younger boys,
too stupid not to be nervous,
laughing, getting their voices
caught by our older boy glares.
We were serious.

Only one could do the act this time,
we decided, another time,
perhaps we all do it,
but this was a holy moment of isolation & separating.

It was my moment.
I directed the boys where to gather,
and how to make a horseshoe around the table.
I had the door's lock checked twice.

I was wearing my suit & my tie,
and thick black shoes & socks & garters.
I held the pig's snout & put two fingers down its mouth.

It was dry & I asked for the oil to be poured on my hand
as it passed in & out of the pigmouth.
I asked that my trousers be taken down.

The oil smelled like rosemary
and my hand started to go smoothly.
I asked someone to hold the snout,
and let another boy remove my jacket.

I would leave on the shirt & tie.
I don't remember why.
It felt formal.
I had to shout "Respect!" to keep the youngers quiet.

I pulled my hand out.
The pig was well-oiled.

I asked that two sturdy candles
be put in its ears & lit,
and the lights be turned off.

There we stood,
my pig, its gape & I.

I held it by its little toes
and moved toward its face.

my porco dio, my berkshire baphomet

I listened to the slow warming slickness of my cock, passing into the mouth of this beautiful dead pig. The candles flared. As I lay inside this pig, I let go of its legs, I started to hum & let my cadre behind hum at my tone. This is the sound that marks me. The room didn't shake, it felt more deeply still, the youngers were crying but still silent. Wax from the candles pooled inside the head.

I asked for two boys to take hold my bare hips, to pull them & then thrust them, delicately, against the mouth of this dead pig. They were clumsy, pushing me too hard, rustling the pig, bashing its snout with my pelvis, I stopped them & took hold again for myself. There I pulled, my fingernails cut in, I bent, I bit into the thick rind on its back, I pulled myself inside the mouth & shouted & came.

I hadn't meant to cum, I had only meant to lay my penis inside of the pig's mouth for the ritual. I had stayed in until the finish because every time I belted into that pig, the world that took a breath & waited for the next. Pressing in was an historical density around which we were re-forming, pull out, our souls withdrew & we were pale like pigs.

My penis grew soft & fell out of the pig's mouth. I stood up & let the other men gather around me & hug me. We hummed once more. The turning & returning of inside & out, of pleasure & desire or thrust & pull, of love & objects, will not be not stopped. I retrieve myself some afternoons & feel, despite all my successes, that I was mistaken in my ideas about the pig & ritual & sex.

I thought sex with this pig would be sex with all the shudders of pure love, sex without the shatters of anxiety. But there is a turn & return too, of rituals & tradition, of the former in vitality & the later in dotage & death.

And I was ritual & the pig was tradition & we mingled & I was young & it was as old as it was ever gonna be, we fucked each other there. And as the cum came, time was rent again & I was set on that moment for mine, the moment I am forced by ecstasy to contemplate again. The sound of the chaps' humming, as I fucked in the mouth
of that pig, vibrated me & set
the tone of my spirit & my life.

I vibrate.

I am that sound.

I am still caught in that belly & bound by those teeth.

My soul speaks in one sound.

I vibrate.

Made in the USA
Lexington, KY
27 November 2016